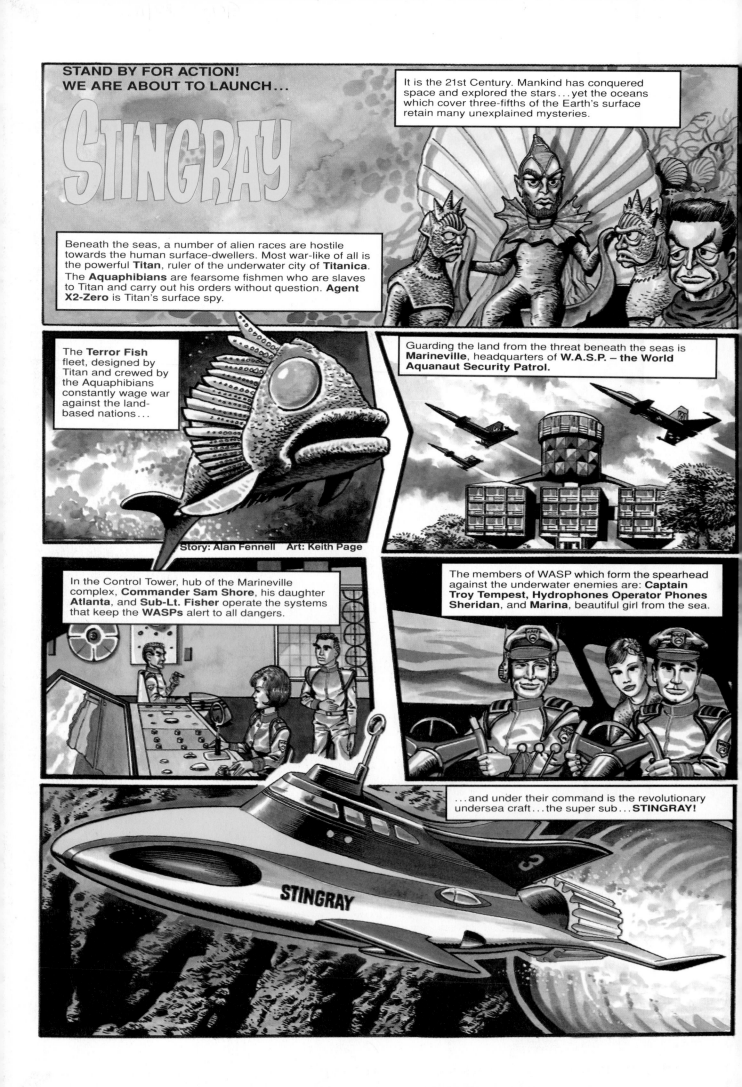

STAND BY FOR ACTION!
WE ARE ABOUT TO LAUNCH...

STINGRAY

It is the 21st Century. Mankind has conquered space and explored the stars...yet the oceans which cover three-fifths of the Earth's surface retain many unexplained mysteries.

Beneath the seas, a number of alien races are hostile towards the human surface-dwellers. Most war-like of all is the powerful **Titan**, ruler of the underwater city of **Titanica**. The **Aquaphibians** are fearsome fishmen who are slaves to Titan and carry out his orders without question. **Agent X2-Zero** is Titan's surface spy.

The **Terror Fish** fleet, designed by Titan and crewed by the Aquaphibians constantly wage war against the land-based nations...

Story: Alan Fennell   Art: Keith Page

Guarding the land from the threat beneath the seas is **Marineville**, headquarters of **W.A.S.P. — the World Aquanaut Security Patrol.**

In the Control Tower, hub of the Marineville complex, **Commander Sam Shore**, his daughter **Atlanta**, and **Sub-Lt. Fisher** operate the systems that keep the WASPs alert to all dangers.

The members of WASP which form the spearhead against the underwater enemies are: **Captain Troy Tempest, Hydrophones Operator Phones Sheridan**, and **Marina**, beautiful girl from the sea.

...and under their command is the revolutionary undersea craft...the super sub...**STINGRAY!**

STINGRAY

STINGRAY

Printed and bound for Ravette Books Limited, 8 Clifford Street, London W1X 1RB, an Egmont Company, by Proost International Bookproduction, Belgium.

ISBN: 1 85304 302 8.

STINGRAY

The World Security submarine Seaprobe is on routine patrol in the Pacific...but danger lurks undetected in the depths. Cold, alien eyes follow the sub's progress.

A missile flashes from the mouth of the Mechanical Fish, and its grotesque crew watch with evil satisfaction...

...as Seaprobe disappears in a searing mass of flame and twisted metal.

The World Security headquarters in Washington D.C. decides this is a job for the **WASPs** and **Commander Shore** orders **Troy Tempest** and **Phones Sheridan** to investigate. Minutes later, *Stingray* knifes out of the Ocean Door.

The route to Seaprobe's last recorded position takes the Super Sub past the lonely island of Lemoy.

From this ramshackle house on the cliff, Surface Agent X20 tracks the WASP vessel's progress and reports to his master, the evil Titan. A Terror Fish is despatched to intercept *Stingray* and captures its crew.

Taken by surprise, *Stingray* falls prey to the Terror Fish missile, crashing to the sea-bed. The impact knocks Troy and Phones unconscious.

Troy wakes to find himself in Titan's throne room on trial for his life! Titan points to a huge fish which stares blankly at Troy from its wall tank.

This is Teufel, the great sea god worshipped by Titan. Legend has it that he only looks on those who are friends of the undersea races. Should he turn away from Troy within one marine minute, then the aquanaut is doomed. The time is almost up when Teufel disdainfully turns his back on Troy.

ina, Titan's silent slave, can watch helplessly as Troy is d guilty of treason. He and es are to be transported by r Fish to the dreaded under- prison of aquatraz for sen- tence to be carried out. perate to escape the tyrant elf, Marina decides to try to help the Terraineans.

At Marineville, concern grows over Stingray's radio silence. Aerial searches have found nothing and Shore orders Battle Stations in case of an attack. The base sinks into its armoured shelter, and deadly Hydromic missiles are put on stand by alert.

Meanwhile, en route to Aquatraz, Marina secretly unties Troy's hands. Once free, he quickly overpowers the guards, holding them at gun-point while Marina frees Phones.

pilot the Fish back to and Marina a line to the sub, which w back to ineville.

That evening, much to the surprise of his girl- friend Atlanta, Troy introduces everyone to the beautiful girl from the sea who is now the latest recruit to Stingary's crew!

7

CONTENTS

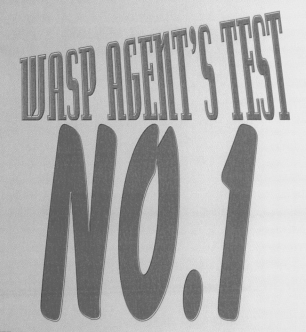

WASP AGENT'S TEST NO.1

Marineville has issued the following questions. This is the first of four special tests in this book, designed to discover what you know about Stingray, and how good a WASP Agent you would be.

1. How fast can Stingray travel?

2. Where is the Standby Lounge?

3. What is the name of Titan's surface agent?

4. Where does he live?

5. Where did Troy first meet Marina?

6. Who are the usual controllers at Marineville?

7. What rank does Troy Tempest hold?

8. What is another name for a Terror Fish?

9. What is the name of the undersea prison?

10. Who is Aphony?

11. Where does he live?

12. What are Commander Shore's christian names?

The answers to test No.1 are on page 45.

POACHER OF THE DEEP

Troy Tempest yawned as he sent *Stingray* flashing through the Pacific depths towards distant Marineville.

"Another routine patrol over. Now for a sleep and a day off.." "Hold your sea-horses, Troy!" Phones cut in, his hand adjusting the headphones. "Emergency call from Control Tower..."

Atlanta's voice came over the cabin speakers. "Tower to *Stingray*...Commander Shore has an urgent assignment for you, Troy." "Okay, Honey," Troy stifled another yawn. "But this had better be something really good or.."

"Or what, Tempest?" roared Commander Shore. "WASPs are on duty twenty-four hours a day!" "Twenty-five he means!" Phones muttered, forgetting his microphone was switched on. "And I don't want any wisecracks from you either, Phones. Now listen carefully."

He told them that reports were coming in of raids on pearl nurseries throughout a large area of the Pacific. Hundreds of thousands of oysters had disappeared over the last few days. The latest report was from the Harikutas, a group of small coral islands at position 47 south-south-west 25.

"Poachers, sir?" Troy asked, interested now.

"Maybe. It's your job to find out, Tempest...get cracking! The Fisheries Commission complains the work of twenty years will be wiped out if these raids go on." "Okay, Commander! We're on our way!"

Troy swung *Stingray* without slackening speed. "Rate six, Phones." As *Stingray* hurtled south by west at maximum speed, Phones pin-pointed the location of the Harikutas on his navigation chart. "Poachers!" he growled. "What's he think we are - gamekeepers?" "If poachers are behind these raids, they're no ordinary poachers," Troy replied thoughtfully. "Not working on that scale...I've got a hunch we may be up against something bigger than we reckon."

Two hours later, *Stingray* surfaced and lay-to about a mile off a group of islands scattered like green and white cakes on the shimmering blue of the ocean. A white concrete building with a radio mast on one of the beaches was the only sign of habitation Troy could see through his glasses.

"Do we go ashore and talk to the guys in charge?" Phones asked.

"No. Could be one of them is working in with whoever's behind this business. We'll investigate below

first, look for clues. What's the depth between the island, Phones?"

Phones consulted his oceangraphs. "Nine fathoms is the deepest those channels go." "Not a lot of space to manoeuvre if we do hit trouble. We'll use swim gear." Troy smiled round at Marina who was standing at his shoulder. "Coming along?" "You just try to stop her!" Phones chuckled as the mysterious girl from the sea nodded her head eagerly.

Troy submerged and brought *Stingray* to a halt on the white sandy bed of the ocean some five hundred yards from the nearest island. He and Phones put on their skin suits and masks and followed Marina out through the airlock. As they swam towards the pearl beds shoals of rainbow-hued fishes darted away. A giant moray eel large enough to swallow an arm whole bared its vicious teeth at them and withdrew into its rock crevice when Troy shone a torch at it. Marina led the way through a coral forest ablaze with colourful blossoms in the sunlight that filtered down through the blue water. And then they saw the oyster cages - or what was left of them.

"Great Neptune!" Troy gasped, swimming nearer to inspect one of them. It had been twisted and torn almost out of recognition - just as if a gigantic tin opener had been at work. "Not very tidy guys,

whoever they are," Phones growled. "I don't get this," Troy said, looking thoughtfully at other cages which had been maltreated in the same crude way "With oxyacetylene flame cutters they could have made a neat job - and a quicker one." They swam on through the channel. Everywhere they looked cages had been ripped open and their contents taken. Here and there a solitary oyster, apparently dropped by the raiders, lay forlorn on the coral bottom, all that were left of thousands that had inhabited the cages the day before.

Suddenly, Marina, who had swum ahead to where the channel opened out into the main ocean, gestured eagerly to Troy and Phones. They joined her and she pointed to a small trail of oysters leading away towards the ocean depths. Troy realised why Marina was so excited. "No cages here," he said. "So they must have dropped these oysters when they were making their getaway. Let's see where the trail leads. Maybe if we can find where they joined their craft, we'll get a clue to who they were " "Or what!" Phones said grimly as they swam off. Troy glanced sharply at him.

"You thinking of Aquaphibians?" "Why not? Titan would get a kick out of robbing these pearl nurseries." Troy frowned. "The scale of the robberies is big enough for him, Phones - but I can't see him

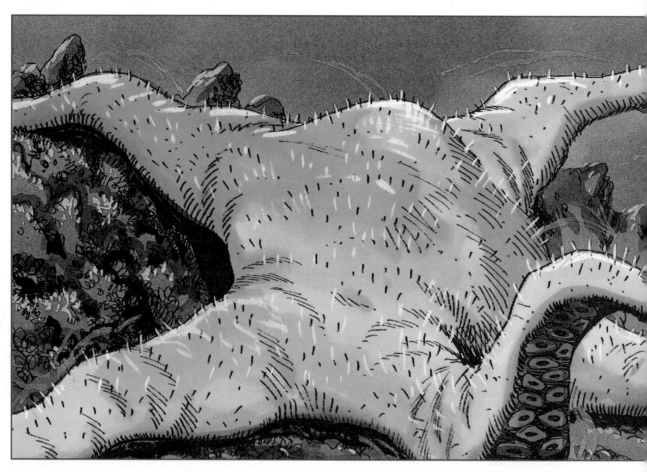

doing it so clumsily."

Presently the trail of oysters vanished near the edge of an ocean ravine. "What now?" Phones asked. "Go back and bring *Stingray* round here," Troy ordered. "Marina and I will see if we can pick up the trail again. If we don't we can be pretty sure this is where they joined their craft."

Phones swam off back the way they had come. Troy and Marina separated, swimming in opposite directions along the edge of the ravine. Troy kept close to the bottom, scanning it carefully as he twisted his way through a many-hued forest of coral and gorgonia. The water was shallow enough here for the sun to give him all the light he needed.

Suddenly he spotted some more oysters, lying on the coral by what appeared to be a greyish rock on which were growing weird plants like wavy fleshy lips. Intent on the oysters he paid little attention to it. But as his flippered foot touched it, he felt it move. Instinctively he tried to push off, but his foot went down between the fleshy lips, and the next instant his ankle was seized in a vice-like grip that wrung a gasp of pain from his lips.

He twisted and looked down and a spasm of fear went through him. What he had taken for a rock was a giant clam - the colossal shellfish that had been the terror of old-time pearl divers. Once a diver was gripped by the leg there was no way he could released himself - and he was held in that

relentless grip until he drowned. Troy knew little short of dynamite would induce the clam to release its hold on him.

He fought off his panic. He couldn't drown while his oxygen lasted and he had friends within call. He forced himself to speak calmly into the hydrophone, not wanting to alarm Phones and bring him hurrying back without *Stingray*. "Marina! I've found something! Come - "

The words froze on his lips. He caught sight of a huge tentacle. But it was unlike any tentacle he had ever seen on any creature under the ocean. It was more like the end of a monstrous cucumber, flat on the underside and covered with hundreds of short spines. The tentacle tip rose slowly, exposing a mass of short tubes with sucker-like discs at the end, all waving in a way that made his blood run cold.

Powerless to move, he watched as the tentacle moved with incredible speed across the coral towards him, dragging itself by its suckers. A second tentacle followed it over the edge of the ravine...a third. Then a huge creature like something out of a nightmare, quite twenty feet across, heaved itself over the edge, trailing two more tentacles. Only then did the truth dawn on Troy. They weren't tentacles - they were the rays or arms of a monster starfish. Helpless in the grip of the clam, he watched the gigantic creature crawling towards him, pulling itself along by its hundreds of tube

feet. He tried to remember what he had read about starfish. Phrases from books he had studied on the marine biology and recognition courses all WASP personnel had to attend.

Voracious creatures...terrible devourers of flesh..No teeth...They distend their stomachs over their victim and...

A ray touched the shell of the giant clam, seemed to explore it intelligently. He swallowed with difficulty. He was flesh! Instinctively his hand sought the knife at his waist. But then he remembered...

If any of the five rays of a starfish is severed, it grows into another starfish...

A second ray had gripped the other half of the clam's shell. The starfish was hauling itself on to the clam, dragging itself towards him. He drew his knife. Even if the starfish became five, at least they wouldn't be big enough to harm him yet. The other three rays were now gripping the clam. There were three clamped to one side of the shell, two to the other side. It was still inching its way towards him. The tip of one of the rays was a foot from him now. But it would be useless just to cut off the tip..

Suddenly he realised the gigantic creature had stopped moving towards him. The minutes sped away. Still it had not moved. But he saw that its rays seemed to be writhing as if muscles inside were working. Another phrase from the books floated through his mind.

The starfish is the oyster's greatest enemy...With three rays clamped to one valve of an oyster, two to the other, it forces it open and devours it...

Incredulously he watched as the huge shells of the clam were pulled slowly apart. He was so fascinated that he didn't realise until he felt Marina tugging at him that the pressure on his foot had eased. With a little gulp of relief he snatched it out of the opening mouth of the clam.

"Ugh!" Phones grunted when he heard the story. "Nice character! So he's our poacher, eh? When he can't get giant clams he has to have oysters by the bushel...What do we do with him - we can't leave him to decimate the oyster beds.." "We're netting him and towing him back to Marineville," decided Troy. "Our marine biologists would never forgive us if we let a specimen like this get away."

Back at Marineville, their strange captive was placed in a huge aquarium in the marine museum. "It's sure a *star* fish!" grinned Phones as he and Troy and Marina watched the giant creature. "But how did it grow to that size?" "One of the back-room boys told me that radio-active waste was dumped in that ravine off the Harikutas some years back," Troy said. "My buddy must have taken some with his diet and it stimulated his growth some. It wouldn't happen again in a thousand years." "That's comforting," Phones grunted. "Once in a while is quite enough, I guess."

THE END

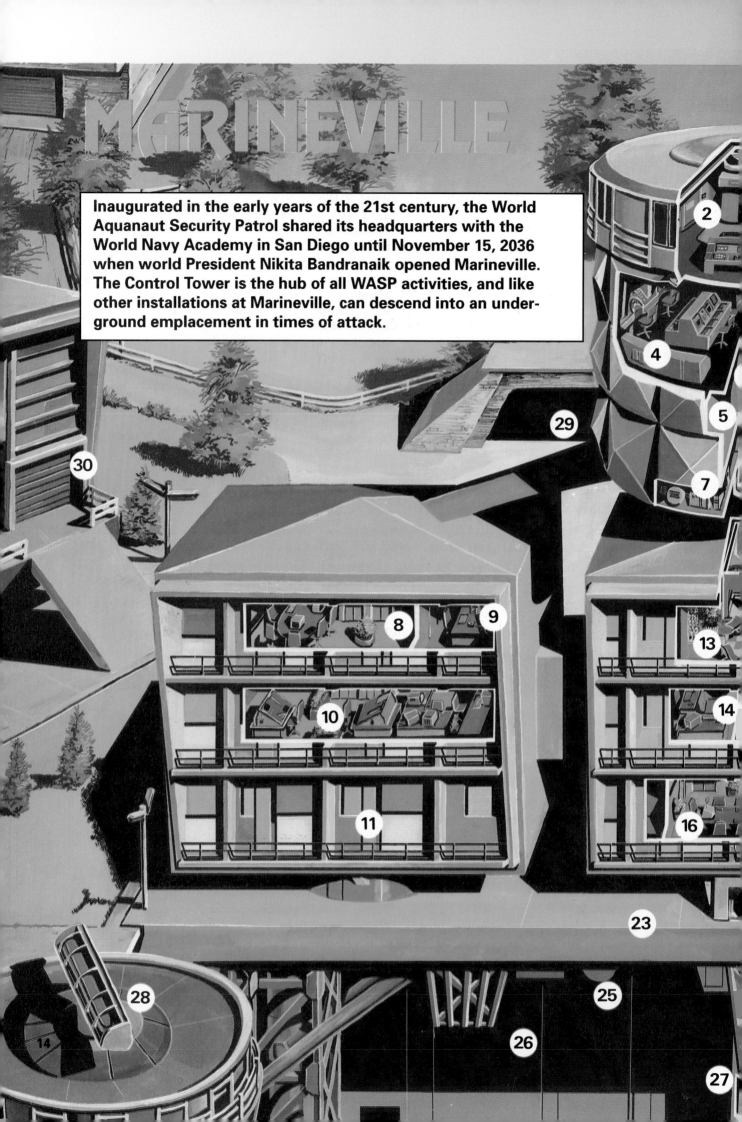

MARINEVILLE

Inaugurated in the early years of the 21st century, the World Aquanaut Security Patrol shared its headquarters with the World Navy Academy in San Diego until November 15, 2036 when world President Nikita Bandranaik opened Marineville. The Control Tower is the hub of all WASP activities, and like other installations at Marineville, can descend into an underground emplacement in times of attack.

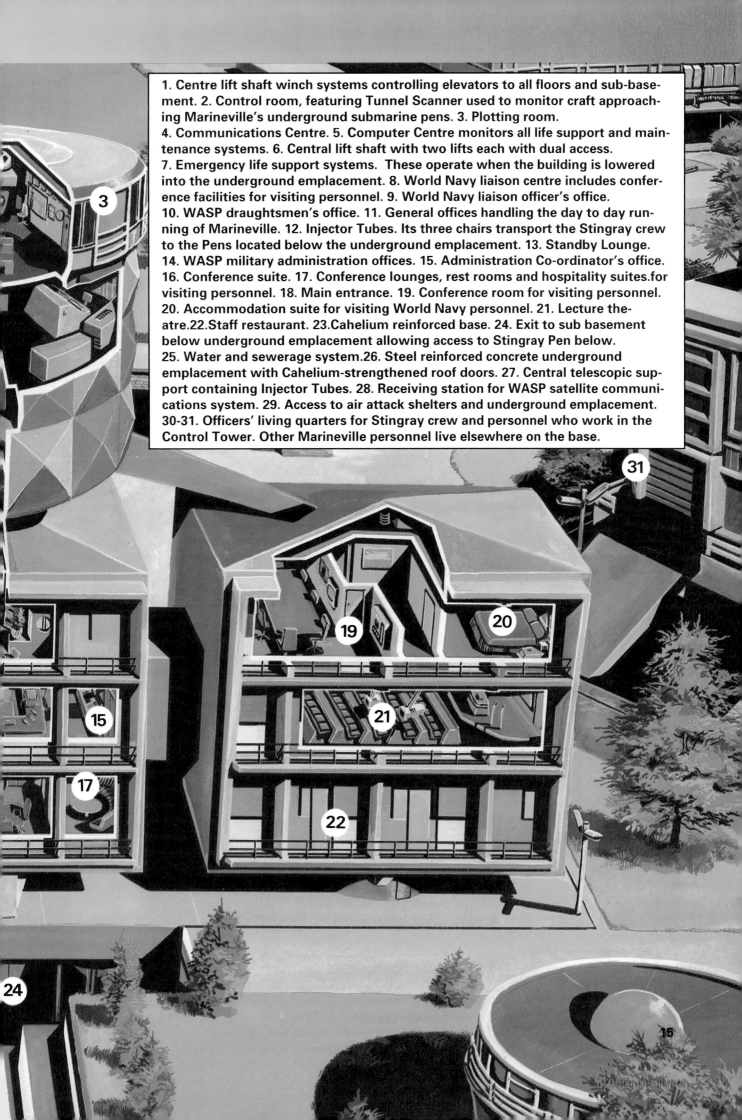

1. Centre lift shaft winch systems controlling elevators to all floors and sub-basement. 2. Control room, featuring Tunnel Scanner used to monitor craft approaching Marineville's underground submarine pens. 3. Plotting room.
4. Communications Centre. 5. Computer Centre monitors all life support and maintenance systems. 6. Central lift shaft with two lifts each with dual access.
7. Emergency life support systems. These operate when the building is lowered into the underground emplacement. 8. World Navy liaison centre includes conference facilities for visiting personnel. 9. World Navy liaison officer's office.
10. WASP draughtsmen's office. 11. General offices handling the day to day running of Marineville. 12. Injector Tubes. Its three chairs transport the Stingray crew to the Pens located below the underground emplacement. 13. Standby Lounge.
14. WASP military administration offices. 15. Administration Co-ordinator's office.
16. Conference suite. 17. Conference lounges, rest rooms and hospitality suites.for visiting personnel. 18. Main entrance. 19. Conference room for visiting personnel.
20. Accommodation suite for visiting World Navy personnel. 21. Lecture theatre.22.Staff restaurant. 23.Cahelium reinforced base. 24. Exit to sub basement below underground emplacement allowing access to Stingray Pen below.
25. Water and sewerage system.26. Steel reinforced concrete underground emplacement with Cahelium-strengthened roof doors. 27. Central telescopic support containing Injector Tubes. 28. Receiving station for WASP satellite communications system. 29. Access to air attack shelters and underground emplacement.
30-31. Officers' living quarters for Stingray crew and personnel who work in the Control Tower. Other Marineville personnel live elsewhere on the base.

STINGRAY

MARINEVILLE, HEADQUARTERS OF WASP—THE WORLD AQUANAUT SECURITY PATROL...

IN THE CONTROL TOWER IS COMMANDER SAM SHORE, HIS DAUGHTER ATLANTA AND SUB-LIEUTENANT JOHN FISHER...

TOWER TO CAPTAIN TEMPEST. MAKE READY FOR ESCORT PATROL DUTY...

TROY, PHONES AND MARINA ARE IN THE STAND-BY LOUNGE.

THE INJECTOR TUBES TAKE TROY, PHONES AND MARINA DOWN THROUGH MARINEVILLE'S MAIN BUILDING...

INJECTOR BAY

Story: Alan Fennell   Art: Keith Page

IN IT'S PEN, STINGRAY IS READY FOR LAUNCH PROCEDURE...

PEN 3 STINGRAY

STINGRAY

LAUNCH STATIONS ARE SOUNDED AND STINGRAY APPROACHES THE OCEAN DOOR...

STINGRAY

STINGRAY'S ROUTINE MISSION— TO ESCORT A MERCHANT FREIGHTER THROUGH HOSTILE WATERS...

PROCEEDING TO RENDEZVOUS POINT. ISLE OF LEMOY ON PORT BEAM...

STINGRAY

SINISTER EYES WATCH STINGRAY'S PROGRESS...

MIGHTY TITAN HAS BEEN WAITING FOR STINGRAY TO LEAVE MARINEVILLE!

Subject: Troy Tempest
Age: 27
Educated World Naval Academy, San Diego
First career detail: Joined Submarine Service - aged 18
Present rank: Captain
Present appointment: Command of WASP vessel *Stingray*

ON A ROUTINE MISSION TO ESCORT A MERCHANT FREIGHTER THROUGH HOSTILE WATERS, STINGRAY PASSES THE ISLE OF LEMOY.

WE HAVE CONTACT WITH THE FREIGHTER, TROY.

RIGHT YOU ARE, PHONES. INCREASING TO RATE 3.

ON THE ISLE OF LEMOY, IN A STRANGE OLD HOUSE, TITAN'S SURFACE AGENT X2-ZERO HAS SEEN THE SUPER SUB...

TITAN MUST BE INFORMED THAT STINGRAY HAS LEFT MARINEVILLE.

LIGHTS FLASH, PANELS SHIFT, TABLES TURN AND THE HOUSE OF LEMOY CONVERTS TO AN INCREDIBLE COMMUNICATIONS CENTRE.

A GIANT MONITOR SCREEN CLEARS TO SHOW TITAN, EVIL RULER OF THE UNDERWATER KINGDOM OF TITANICA.

WHAT HAVE YOU TO REPORT, X2-ZERO?

STINGRAY HAS JUST PASSED THE ISLAND, MIGHTY TITAN.

EXCELLENT! I HAVE PLANS FOR TROY TEMPEST AND HIS FRIENDS. KEEP TRACK OF STINGRAY... AND DO NOT FAIL ME!

I WILL FOLLOW IN MY UNDERWATER CRAFT, YOUR MAJESTY...

SOON WE WILL KNOW IF THE NEW WEAPON AT MY COMMAND IS SUCCESSFUL!

Subject: Phones -
George Lee Sheridan
Age: 31
Educated: Various
schools
First career detail:
Various jobs - soldier of
fortune
Present rank:
Lieutenant
Present appointment:
Hydrophone Operator -
Stingray

STINGRAY IS ON A ROUTINE ESCORT DUTY WHEN TITAN DECIDES TO TEST A NEW WEAPON. ON THE ISLE OF LEMOY, SURFACE AGENT X2-ZERO PREPARES TO TRACK THE SUPER SUB...

X2-ZERO LEAVES THE ISLAND...

I MUST KEEP A SAFE DISTANCE AWAY. STINGRAY HAS VERY POWERFUL OBSERVATION EQUIPMENT...

STINGRAY

3

FREIGHTER DEAD AHEAD, TROY...

CLOSE IN, PHONES—AND MATCH VESSEL'S SPEED.

DEEP BENEATH THE WAVES IS THE STRANGE AND POWERFUL CITY OF TITANICA...

TITAN HAS CALLED A SIMPERING SCIENTIST TO HIS PALACE...

THE TIME HAS COME TO TEST YOUR NEW COMPOUND, GILFIN. IF IT FAILS— YOU DIE!

Script by Alan Fennell   Art: Keith Page

LAUNCH THE TERROR FISH.!

Subject: Marina
Age: 19 marine years
Educated: Underwater city of Pacifica
Biographic detail: Rescued from Titanica by Troy Tempest
Present appointment: Crew member of *Stingray*

TITAN HAS A NEW SECRET WEAPON AND LAUNCHES A TERROR FISH TO INTERCEPT STINGRAY...

TROY – I'M PICKING UP A SOUNDING. SOME SORT OF UNDERWATER CRAFT IS HEADING OUR WAY...

LET'S TAKE A LOOK, PHONES. FLOOD "Q"!

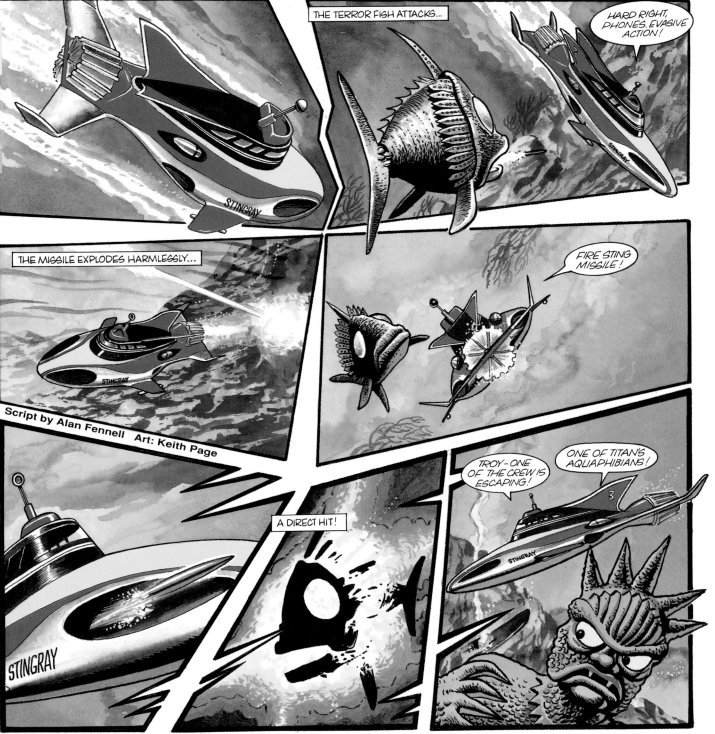

THE TERROR FISH ATTACKS...

HARD RIGHT, PHONES. EVASIVE ACTION!

THE MISSILE EXPLODES HARMLESSLY...

FIRE STING MISSILE!

Script by Alan Fennell   Art: Keith Page

A DIRECT HIT!

TROY – ONE OF THE CREW IS ESCAPING!

ONE OF TITAN'S AQUAPHIBIANS!

Subject: Atlanta Shore
Age: 23
Educated: University of Southern California
Present rank: Lieutenant
Present appointment: Deputy controller - Marineville Control Tower

STINGRAY AND A TERROR FISH DO BATTLE, BUT WHEN TROY TEMPEST GOES IN PURSUIT OF AN ESCAPING AQUAPHIBIAN, HIS WET-SUIT IS SLASHED...

IN STINGRAY, PHONES REACTS...

DON'T WORRY, SKIPPER I'M COMING TO GET YOU!

BUT MARINA HAS ALREADY LEFT STINGRAY...

PHONES HELPS TROY ABOARD AND SOON STINGRAY IS RACING BACK TO MARINEVILLE...

STINGRAY

Story: Alan Fennell   Art: Keith Page

SOON TROY IS RECOVERING...

WHAT HAPPENED? MARINA... SAY— MY WET-SUIT HAS BEEN CUT...

NEXT SECOND, OINK THE PET SEAL LEAPS ON TOP OF TROY...

HEY, OINK! YOU'VE NEVER WELCOMED ME LIKE THIS!

21

Subject: John Horatio Fisher
Age: 24
Educated: World Navy Cadet School
Present rank: Lieutenant
Present appointment: Operator - Marineville Control Tower

TROY TEMPEST HAS AN UNDERSEA FIGHT WITH AN AQUAPHIBIAN. THE FISHMAN ESCAPES, BUT NOT BEFORE HE HAS SLASHED TROY'S WET-SUIT. WITH THE SKIPPER SAFELY BACK ON BOARD, STINGRAY RETURNS TO BASE...

IN THE CONTROL TOWER, TROY RECOVERS QUICKLY...

IT'S A PITY YOU DIDN'T HAVE A CHANCE TO ANALYSE THAT ORANGE CLOUD, TEMPEST...

I'M SORRY, COMMANDER. I HAD MY ARMS FULL OF AQUAPHIBIAN!

OK, TROY, HAND YOUR GEAR OVER TO THE LAB BOYS FOR TESTS... AND GET SOME REST.

DON'T FORGET TROY, YOU'RE HAVING DINNER WITH FATHER AND ME TONIGHT...

TROY RESTS FOR THE REMAINDER OF THE DAY...

GET AWAY, YOU MUTTS! WHY ARE YOU FOLLOWING ME?

WELL, THANK YOU, TROY. COME ON IN...

I SEEM TO BE ATTRACTING EVERY DOG AND CAT IN MARINEVILLE!

Story: Alan Fennell Art: Keith Page

SIT DOWN AT THE TABLE TROY. DINNER WON'T BE LONG.

SURE, TROY... TELL ME MORE ABOUT THAT TERROR FISH ATTACK!

SUDDENLY...

WHAT THE..!

AND OUTSIDE THE OCEAN DOOR...

MARINEVILLE
FACTFILE
NO.7

Subject: Titan
Age: 130 marine years
Position: Ruler of underwater kingdom Titanica
Ambition: The destruction of Marineville, Troy Tempest and *Stingray*. Seeks control of the Earth

AFTER A BATTLE WITH ONE OF TITAN'S AQUAPHIBIANS, TROY TEMPEST RETURNS TO MARINEVILLE. THEN, AT THE OCEAN DOOR THAT LEADS TO MARINEVILLE, DANGEROUS SEA CREATURES GATHER...

IN TITANICA...

YOU FOOLS CANNOT BE TRUSTED TO DO ANYTHING CORRECTLY!

BUT, YOUR GREATNESS, OUR POOR FRIEND HERE FOUGHT HARD AGAINST THE ACCURSED TEMPEST...

TITAN'S ATTENTION IS DRAWN TO A MONITOR SCREEN...

THAT'S THE ENTRANCE TO MARINEVILLE...

AND SEE, MIGHTY TITAN, THE SHARKS HAVE BEEN ATTRACTED...

THE ORANGE CLOUD PENETRATED TEMPEST'S WETSUIT. THE CREATURES WANT TO BE NEAR HIM!

THE SECRET WEAPON WORKS! NEXT TIME WE WILL HIT STINGRAY!

MEANWHILE, TROY IS BEING EXAMINED IN MARINEVILLE'S HOSPITAL...

YOU'RE CLEAR, TROY. WE DON'T KNOW WHY THE ANIMALS AND FISH HAVE BEEN BOTHERING YOU...

GUESS WE'LL KNOW MORE WHEN WE GET MY WETSUIT TEST RESULTS THROUGH...

IN THE CONTROL TOWER...

UNLESS WE CLEAR THE OCEAN DOOR STINGRAY AND MOST OF MARINEVILLE'S SUBMARINE FLEET ARE TRAPPED.

VERY WELL, ATLANTA—TRAIN THE DEFENCE MISSILES ON THOSE BEAUTIES AND SCARE THEM AWAY.

BUT BE CAREFUL—WE DON'T WANT TO DAMAGE THE TUNNEL ENTRANCE!

MARINEVILLE FACT FILE NO.8

Subject: X-20
Age: 107 marine years
Position: Suspected surface agent for Titanica. Born in a city conquered by Titan, he is now one of Titan's closest helpers

AFTER SWIMMING THROUGH A STRANGE ORANGE CLOUD TROY TEMPEST RETURNS TO MARINEVILLE... ATTRACTING FIERCE UNDERSEA CREATURES. UNAWARE THAT THE CLOUD IS TITAN'S LATEST SECRET WEAPON, THE WASPS TRY TO CLEAR THE BLOCKED OCEAN DOOR...

IN MARINEVILLE'S CONTROL TOWER...

THE WET-SUIT TESTS SHOW YOU WERE DRENCHED IN SOME SORT OF CHEMICAL. THAT'S WHAT ATTRACTED THE ANIMALS AND FISH...

COULD HAVE BEEN THAT ORANGE CLOUD THAT CAME FROM THE TERROR FISH MISSILE...

GET OUT THERE AND INVESTIGATE, TROY. TITAN'S UP TO SOMETHING - AND I WANT TO KNOW ABOUT IT!

Script by Alan Fennell   Art: Keith Page

TITAN'S AGENT X20 IS WAITING...

STINGRAY HAS BEEN LAUNCHED, MIGHTY TITAN.

THIS TIME WE WILL NOT MISS STINGRAY! GO - ATTACK!

Continued on page 50

THE SUPER SUB

On routine patrol in the waters near Titanica, Stingray comes to rest on the ocean bed. Shutting down the motors, Troy decides to listen for Terror Fish activity. On this occasion there was no enemy activity, but the danger is always present and the WASPs have to keep a constant watch on this hostile area of the sea.

TERROR FISH

Just released from the Marineville Press Office, this drawing of one of Titan's Mechanical Fish has been prepared from reports of marine engineers who have examined a "Tin Terror" captured recently by Captain Troy Tempest. The craft is built from fused coral Titanium, an undersea material similar to Cahelium Extract X that is used in Stingray's construction. An average speed of 550 knots has been recorded. The Terror Fish are only a part of Titan's fleet: other craft include large cargo vessels and smaller single seat mini-submarines, all built to resemble fish or other ocean creatures.

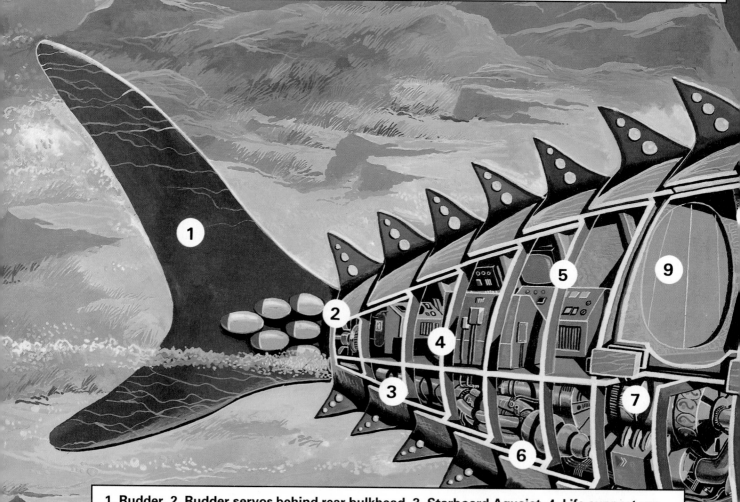

1. Rudder. 2. Rudder servos behind rear bulkhead. 3. Starboard Aquajet. 4. Life support systems monitor internal atmosphere and cabin pressure. 5. Radio, sonar and Aquascan console and engine monitor system. 6. Starboard turboflow Aquajet propulsion system, powered by Grananol fuel. 7. Generators supplying power to auxiliary propulsion unit. 8. Grananol fuel and ballast tanks. 9. Access hatch from aft cabin to airlocks. 10. Airlock, with entry hatches on both sides of craft. 11. Access hatch to passenger or cargo bay and control cabin beyond. 12. Optional passenger seating: this area can be used to carry small cargoes if seating is removed. 13. Stabilising fin with integrated video periscope (retracted). 14. Armour plated hull, constructed of fused coral Titanium with integrated navigation lights. 15. Quartz-strengthened viewing port "eyes". 16. Viewing port rim features lighting units which can be focused through the thickness of the quartz eyes to form a single searchlight beam. 17. Servo systems operating port and starboard stabilising fins. 18. Main control and central computer. 19. Main armament of six missiles. 20. Hinged lower jaw in dropped position in readiness for instant missile release. 21. Forward Aquascan sensor, which also incorporates laser beam gun for removing obstacles. 22. Atmosphere recycling control and monitoring console.

THE SILENT PREDATOR

A story by Helen McCarthy

"So the Government has had warnings not to blast in this area, Troy."

"Yeah, that's why we're here, in case anyone tries to interfere with the mineral survey ship. If there are any unfriendly craft around I want to know what they're up to, so pin back your ears and keep listening, Phones."

Suddenly *Stingray* was rocked by shock waves as an explosion ripped the sea-bed about half a mile away.

"You know, Troy," drawled the hydrophone operator when *Stingray* steadied, "seems to me like we could be in more danger from those guys on the survey than from any unfriendly craft."

Troy frowned. "All the blasting sure isn't helping the marine life much. Is that why you're unhappy, Marina?"

The girl from the sea nodded, staring sadly out of the viewscreen. Then, suddenly, she pointed beyond the survey craft.

A yawning gap opened in the ocean floor. Out of it, silent and menacing, there rose a dark shadow like a huge shark.

For an instant the survey site was engulfed in a flash of light so intense that

the *Stingray* crew were blinded, and the Super Sub rocked under the impact of a powerful explosion.

By the time Troy's vision cleared, the shadowy shark-craft had vanished. Of the mineral survey team, nothing remained but debris tumbling slowly down to the ocean bed.

After reporting the disaster to Commander Shore, *Stingray* combed the area for signs of the strange craft without success, until Phones spotted a long crack in the ocean floor and a faint greenish light filtering through it. Kitted out in wet-suits and aqualungs, Troy and Phones swam out to investigate.

A trail of bubbles rose from a rock pile. Underneath was a grey metal plate with a crescent-shaped recess in its centre. When Troy touched it the plate swung upwards, revealing a tunnel about two metres wide, lit by a faint greenish glow, going down-wards into darkness. Silently, Troy and Phones swam in.

After what seemed like an age, they sur-faced in a large underground chamber. Troy and Phones reached for the pistols in their holsters as they broke the surface - then stopped and stared. Standing at the poolside was the most beautiful girl either of them had ever seen, flanked by six of the ugliest sea-creatures imaginable.

"Welcome to Neo-Atlantis, gentlemen. I'm Nadia Emanon. My father sent me to welcome you." She noticed their horrified expressions as they gazed at the creatures behind her, and laughed. "You mustn't mind the Calibans. They're really very friendly. They're just here to take that heavy breathing equipment so that you won't have to haul it around - they'll keep it here for you. Oh, and your guns - we don't carry weapons in Neo-Atlantis."

She led them down a long corridor, seemingly lit by daylight even though they must be far under the sea-bed, to a huge door with the crescent symbol in the cen-tre. Nadia passed her hand across the symbol and the door slid back. Beyond it was a square lined with tall buildings, streets leading off it, looking just like a city on the land.

"Atlantis!" gasped Troy.

"Neo-Atlantis!" said a voice from behind them. "Old Atlantis was almost completely destroyed by volcanoes many centuries ago."

They turned to see a tall man with piercing eyes of the same blue as Nadia's and a neat black beard. He held out his hand. "I'm Doctor Emanon, President of Neo-Atlantis - and Nadia's father. Come up to my office and we'll talk."

"You mean you used to be a member of the WASPs?"

"Yes, Captain Tempest - in fact I was on the scientific team who designed that beautiful craft of yours."

The doctor nodded at one of the bank of viewscreens lining one wall of his office, where *Stingray* could be seen on the ocean bed.

"My wife was a brilliant engineer, but she died in a terrible accident caused by our tampering with the forces of Nature. I vowed then to leave the service and devote my life to bringing up my daughter and trying to preserve the delicate balance of undersea life."

Doctor Emanon's eyes narrowed as he continued. "I was working as a scientist on a marine life survey ship when it sank. The few survivors would have died if the Neo-Atlanteans hadn't found our liferaft. We became part of their society and ten years ago they honoured me by electing me president. Now, all our great scientific

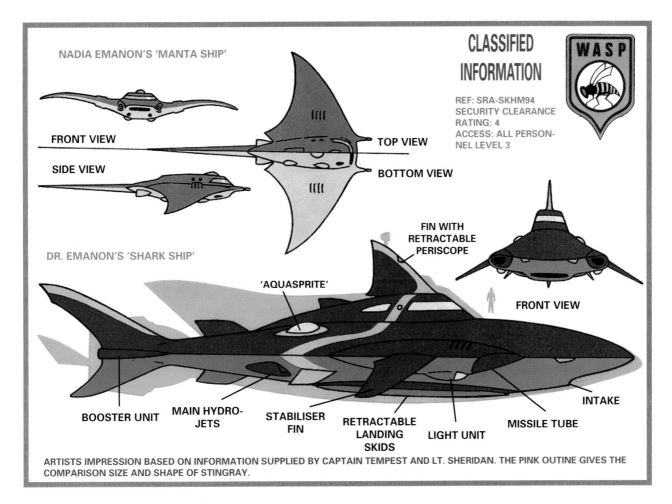

NADIA EMANON'S 'MANTA SHIP'

FRONT VIEW

SIDE VIEW

TOP VIEW

BOTTOM VIEW

FIN WITH RETRACTABLE PERISCOPE

DR. EMANON'S 'SHARK SHIP'

'AQUASPRITE'

FRONT VIEW

BOOSTER UNIT

MAIN HYDRO-JETS

STABILISER FIN

RETRACTABLE LANDING SKIDS

LIGHT UNIT

MISSILE TUBE

INTAKE

ARTISTS IMPRESSION BASED ON INFORMATION SUPPLIED BY CAPTAIN TEMPEST AND LT. SHERIDAN. THE PINK OUTINE GIVES THE COMPARISON SIZE AND SHAPE OF STINGRAY.

resources are devoted to preserving the life of the seas and protecting it from the ignorant and greedy."

"And you put the mineral survey craft that you sank in that category?"

"Unfortunately, Captain, your government and scientists ignored our warnings and offers of help and went ahead with random blasting and mining. I had hoped that they had sent you here to discuss our offers.

"If they had gone on blasting in the area a huge fault in the sea-bed would have become dangerously unstable, perhaps even burst. I could not put the lives of a few people above all the living creatures in this part of the ocean. It's my primary duty to defend Neo-Atlantis and its under-sea life."

"But you killed World Government personnel, sir, said Troy. "I'm afraid my duty is to place you under arrest for murder and take you back to Marineville for trial."

Troy's hand dropped to his belt - then he remembered that his pistol had been taken when they entered Neo-Atlantis.

Doctor Emanon smiled. "You see, Captain, you have no means of enforcing your rather hasty decision. May I suggest that you reconsider?"

"Sir, I may not be able to take you in now," Troy answered, "but when I get back to Marineville and report this the WASPs will send a force to bring you in. If we have to blow up the whole ocean to get you, we will!"

Doctor Emanon shook his head sadly. "There speaks the typical arrogant terrainean. What gives you humans the right to destroy the creatures of the sea for your own ends?"

He pressed a button on the control console on his desk; a door slid open and four Calibans came in. "I regret that you have made it impossible for me to let you leave at present. I must ask you to accompany the guards. We'll talk again tomorrow, when you've had a chance to reconsider."

Outside, in the corridor, Troy nudged Phones and gestured at their escort. Phones nodded, and at the same moment lunged forward, cannoning into both guards, while Troy spun back to the two behind.

After a moment's frantic scuffling they were off, running down the corridor to an open door and out into the square. The huge door by which they had entered was closed, but a small gate beside it was ajar.

It seemed an age before they reached the pool from which they had entered Neo-Atlantis. Their pistols and airtanks were still where they had been left; Troy and Phones hurried into the water and down the long undersea tunnel.

Only when they were back in *Stingray's* control cabin with an anxious Marina did Troy break the silence.

"Rate six for Marineville, Phones," Troy said urgently. "We're going to make sure that madman is brought to justice."

"Don't speak too soon, Troy," warned Phones. "I'm picking up his signature tune again!"

As Phones spoke the dark shape of Emanon's craft appeared in their viewscreen. For a few seconds, no-one moved, then a pair of silver darts were speeding through the water towards *Stingray*.

"Ok, Phones, let's get out of here!"

"They're coming too fast, skipper - I can't shake 'em!"

"Then let's see how they are at air travel!" said Troy through clenched teeth. "I'm taking her out!"

Aiming *Stingray's* nose upwards Troy took her speeding towards the light. As she knifed up and out of the water in a glittering shower of spray the missiles sped straight on; as she fell back towards the surface and plunged into the depths they exploded harmlessly behind her.

"Troy, I'm getting another sounding!" shouted Phones. "Maybe he's calling up reinforcements."

A small golden craft shaped like a manta ray cut between them and the shark. Nadia's voice came over the radio.

"Captain Tempest, get out of here and don't come back. My father is a good man, and he'll fight for what be believes in just

as you will. I don't want him to have any more deaths on his conscience. Father, if you want to destroy *Stingray* you'll have to go through me first."

"Nadia, please don't interfere. I have to protect our people.."

"If we can't protect our ocean without killing in cold blood then we're no better than the Terraineans! Back off, Father. Tempest, what are you hanging around for?"

Troy nodded to Phones and *Stingray* thrust through the water. Nadia's manta moved like a shadow, keeping itself between *Stingray* and the shark-ship. As *Stingray* picked up speed, another missile sped from the shark, to be destroyed by a burst of fire from the manta.

As *Stingray* sped on they heard a series of explosions behind them, but they did not look back.

"Yes, I knew this Doctor Emanon." Sam Shore's expression was thoughtful.

"I remember his wife - a terrible tragedy. You used to play with their little girl, Atlanta - do you remember her?"

"Only vaguely," replied Atlanta. "I remember we used to have great fun. What's she like now, Troy?"

"Beautiful. Brave. Crazy. How can she believe her father can get away with murder?"

"Now hold on, Troy! It's not just her father - it's a whole city, remember. He was telling the truth about warning our government of the dangers of blasting - they received a whole series of messages on coded wavebands, but it was hushed up to avoid a panic. And he was right about that ocean fault, too. The World Government has decided to take no further action."

"No further action! But - "

"That's the end of the matter, Captain," growled the Commander. "The decision's out of our hands. But personally I don't think we've seen the last of Doctor Emanon."

"And I'm pretty sure, if I know you, Troy," said Atlanta acidly, "that you haven't seen the last of his daughter, either!"

THE END

TITANICA

1. Terror Fish standby for immediate launch. 2. Hydraulic Terror Fish launch systems. 3. Telescopic airlock from travel tube terminus to Terror Fish port entry hatch. 4. Terminus for underground travel tube system. 5. Terror Fish manufacturing plant. 6. Factory airlock. 7. Geo-thermal power plant converts volcanic energy deep below the earth's crust into electrical power. 8. Power plant monitoring room. 9. Terminus for underground travel tube. 10. Military administration headquarters. 11. Weapons research laboratories. 12. Sonar scan early warning tower, one of ten around Titanica. 13. Sonar scan monitoring room. 14. Computer centre and civil administration block. 15. Public conference facility. 16. Ruling council chamber. 17. Living accommodation for military command personnel. 18. Terror Fish pens (one of eight located throughout the undersea kingdom. 19. Throne room of one of Titan's several palaces. 20. Prison and interrogation cells. 21. Fused coral Titanium-strengthened travel tube. 22. Secret police monitoring room. 23. Secret police offices, equipment stores. 24. One of many termini for travel tubes linking Titanica's installations. 25. High speed travel tube car. 26. Part of Titanica's defence ring; underwater interceptor missiles placed around the city boundaries, linked by travel tubes. 27. Hydraulic doors disguising the positions of missile emplacements.

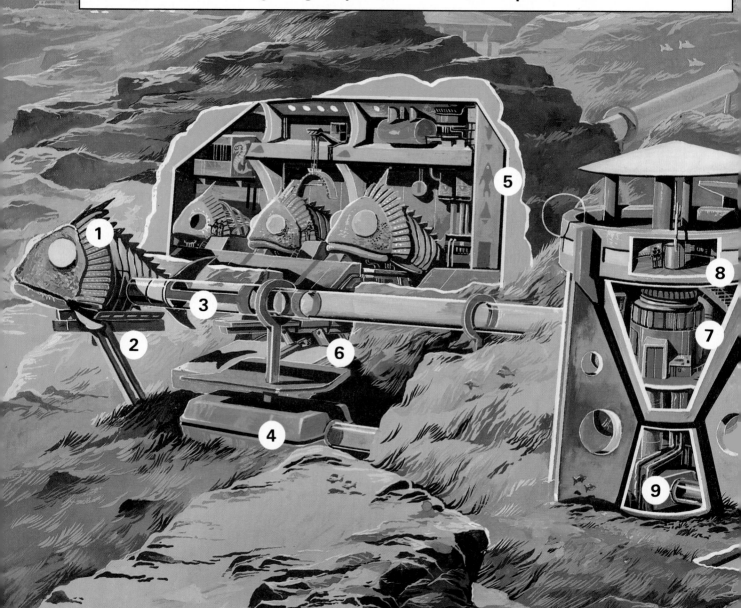

This view of Titanica is based on reports from WASP undercover agents operating in Titan's capital. Very little is known about the city or its inhabitants. It appears to be several kilometres wide in an undisclosed location beneath the Pacific Ocean, some 5,000 fathoms below the surface. Much of the city is built beneath the sea-bed, with only selected structures such as power plants, early warning towers and some living accommodation appearing at sea-bed level. Travel tubes connect these buildings with each other and the subterranean installations, some of which lead to Terror Fish launchers on the city boundaries.

Graham Bleathman

THE INVISIBLE TERROR

"Hi, Atlanta," Troy Tempest grinned cheerfully at Commander Shore's auburn-haired daughter as he and Phones entered the control room of the World Aquanaut Security Patrol at Marineville.

"Got any work for a couple of - "

"Quiet, Troy," Atlanta warned. "Urgent hydrophone message coming through."

"WASP 16 calling Commander Shore!" intoned a voice from the loudspeakers. "Terror Fish sighted position 38 south-south-west 13 - last known location of surface freighter *Lancia*. Proceeding to - "

The voice suddenly cut off and the speakers went dead. Commander Shore leaned forward and stabbed at a button. "Shore calling WASP 16!" he yelled into the microphone. "WASP 16 - come in!" The speakers remained silent. Shore sank back in his hover chair. Troy moved forward.

"That was Pete Webber's vessel, Commander. What's this all about? That message said a Terror Fish. That means - "

"Yeah! It means that shark Titan's up to his dirty tricks again." Shore's deep-set eyes seemed to stab steel shafts at Troy . "You've been on vacation, Tempest. Guess you don't know about the latest trouble. Brief him, Atlanta."

Atlanta told Troy that in the last forty-eight hours reports had been coming into Marineville base of mysterious disappearances of surface vessels from freighter lanes in the South Pacific. Four had vanished without trace. Troy protested. "But a hundred thousand ton atomic freighter can't just disappear, Atlanta - even if its drive explodes! Even a Sting missile leaves some trace of its victim." "We've had patrol vessels on the job ever since the first report came in, Tempest," the Commander cut in tersely. "They

haven't found a scrap of wreckage."

"But how?" "That, Tempest" growled Shore, "is what you're going to find out. Proceed to position 38 south south-west 13 immediately."

Ten minutes later, with Troy, Phones and Marina aboard, *Stingray* slid out through the Ocean Door of the WASP base and sped south by west.

As he neared position 38 south-south-west 13, Troy cut his speed. Sound scanners and video eyes working, Stingray cruised in an ever contracting spiral downwards through the clear ocean depths, but there was no trace of wreckage from patrol vessel sixteen.

"I just don't get it," Troy said. "Let's go topside."

As they broke surface, the brassy sun was high over the Pacific. The ocean was as smooth as a vast sheet of burnished steel. "Just right for a swim," Phones said. "If it wasn't for the sharks."

Marina caught at Troy's arm eagerly and made quick signs. Troy frowned. "She's right, Phones! We didn't see any sharks while we were circling. We saw precious few fish either in the

upper levels."

Hold it, Troy!" Phones cut it. "All-vessels call coming in from base."

"Calling all WASPs! Emergency! All vessels in areas 37 to 40 proceed immediately to Hawakiti Island. Stand by to assist survivors."

"That's us, Troy!" Phones said. "We're not twenty miles from Hawakiti right now."

"Guess this takes priority, Phones," Troy grunted, with a last look at the spot where Webber's vessel had disappeared. "Let's go."

Hawakiti Island was a Pacific play-ground, a holiday paradise of swaying palms and silvery beaches and blue lagoons. As *Stingray* raced towards it over the calm sea, Troy stared in amazement. The big main lagoon was crowded with craft laden down with frightened holiday-makers. Canoes, sailing dinghies, yachts, speed-boats. Some were moving out through the gap in the reef. Hydroplanes were taking off. Frantic figures were racing down the wide beaches and plunging into the water.

Like a sinister backcloth to that panic-stricken scene, a great pall of white dust hung over the island; above it the tops of the palms swayed... beyond them rose the tall pinkie-white coraline bulk of a luxury hotel. Even as Troy watched, the building quivered visibly against the hot blue sky, then crumpled like a sand castle into the dust fog below.

"Great Neptune!" Phones yelled. "It must be an earthquake, Troy!"

Troy glanced at the control panel. "This isn't an earthquake," he said tersely. "The seismograph isn't recording anything. Besides, the sea would be agitated - and it's as calm as a pond."

Marina seized his arm urgently. "What's wrong?" he demanded. She screwed up her pretty face in a grimace and put her fingers to her ears as if to shut out an excruciating noise.

"You mean you can hear something?" he asked, puzzled.

"Well, there's enough racket going on." Marina's long, sea-coloured tresses tossed as she shook her head vigorously.

"Not that noise?" he growled. "Then what?" She pointed to the far side of the island, hidden by a dust pall.

"Okay, Marina!" he said. "Guess you must be on to something. You can hear things we surface people can't."

Troy changed course and sped round the island. Other WASP patrol vessels were racing over the horizon to answer the emergency call and he felt he could leave the frantic holiday-makers to them. Suddenly Marina squeezed his shoulder and pointed ahead, again screwing up her face in the anguished expression.

"Gee, look at the sea!" Phones exclaimed. "It's kinda boiling just in one spot."

Instinctively Troy's glance went to the island. The reef was high just there, and the top of it was crumbling into powder, leaving a gaping hole, as if an invisible monster was boring its way through the coral. "This is it!" he said. "Stand by! We'll submerge and investigate."

Stingray slid smoothly beneath the calm surface, making towards the spot where the sea was agitated.

"What depth have we got to manoeuvre in, Phones?"

"The asdic reading is - " Phones broke off, pointing. "Look, Troy! Right ahead!"

Troy's eyes narrowed as he saw a dim object looming up, heading towards *Stingray*.

"Terror Fish!" Troy growled. "I'm betting it's causing that trouble on Hawakiti."

"Look, Troy!" Phones gasped. "Look how the water's agitated in front of it - just like its eyes are sending out an energy ray. Must be some new diabolical invention of Titan's."

The crew of the fish must have become aware of *Stingray's* approach. Normally they would have fled rather than risk being struck by the deadly Sting missiles *Stingray* carried - but now the enemy vessel swung as if to meet *Stingray's* challenge head on.

Troy acted at once. "Hold tight!" he barked. "I'm taking no chances. Crash dive!"

Stingray hurtled down towards the ocean bed, all motors driving at full pressure. Looking up, Troy realised he had been not a second too soon. Above him the water was violently agitated. Through the swirling bubbles he saw the sinister shape of the fish swinging as if to get on his tail.

"Stand by Sting missile!" he yelled to Phones bringing *Stingray* up and round, squeezing the last gram of speed out of the drive. He saw the Terror Fish dive down behind him, its great eyes glaring malevolently and seeming to boil the water before them. Desperately he swung *Stingray* again, his face grim. It was destroy or be destroyed. But he would have been more confident of the outcome of that strange undersea battle if he had known just what he was up against. What colossal power had the evil scientists of Titanica harnessed.? What was it that

could strike swiftly and silently and destroy huge ships and buildings as effectively as if they had been atomised? Silently? That wasn't quite true. Maybe surface folk couldn't hear the weapon - but Marina could! Silt was swirling up from the bottom, no doubt disturbed by the enemy vessel's mystery weapon. It drifted like a fog through the water, obscuring Troy's vision.

Suddenly Phones gave a warning yell.

"Got a sounding, Troy! Something dead ahead!"

In that same instant Troy saw the glaring eyes. At this range he couldn't fail. "Launch Sting missile, Phones!" he shouted. The second the missile left *Stingray*, Troy slammed his vessel into another crash dive. "Dead on target!" Phones exulted, looking up at the wickedly slim projectile speeding straight for one evil eye of the Aquaphibian's craft.

"Good shot, Pho -" Troy broke off, gasping.

Suddenly there was no missile. It had disintegrated before his eyes. Troy didn't try to think it out. The Terror Fish was diving after *Stingray*. If they got within range with that weapon..

"How much water have we got, Phones?" he snapped.

"Gauge indicates sixty fathoms, Troy. But according to the charts there's a subterranean canyon a hundred fathoms deep half a mile west - a box canyon."

"I know the one! Hold tight!" Troy said. "I'm going to lead those Aquaphibians a dance. If I can only keep them off my tail.."

Again and again the Terror Fish darted at the Super Sub, its mysterious deadly weapon boiling the water ahead of it. Again and again *Stingray* literally escaped by the skin of its hull. But each manoeuvre was skilfully planned by Troy to bring the combatants closer to that deep underwater canyon.

Phones was sweating. "Troy! What the - ?"

"Where's that canyon?" Troy snapped.

"We're right over it now. But if you dive down there we'll be trapped." He was jerked back in his seat with a sickening impact as *Stingray* shot down like a rocket into the murky depths of the canyon.

Caught by surprise, the Aquaphibians in the mechanical fish lost water. But they quickly swung and dived in pursuit. Phones' heart was in his throat when he saw the floor of the canyon rushing up to meet him. He gulped with relief as Troy pulled out of the dive just in time to miss a huge boulder.

"He's gone nuts!" he muttered. "He shoulda taken a longer vacation - TROY!" He pointed ahead to where a black cliff rose steeply before them.

"Take it easy, Phones," Troy said calmly. "That's what I was aiming for. This is the payoff -one way or the other."

At the last vital moment, Troy pulled *Stingray's* nose up and over. Phones shut his eyes, not daring to look. *Stingray* climbed almost vertically, parallel with the cliff wall. The Aquaphibian pilot seemed to see the danger and tried to climb too. But it was too late. A gaping hole appeared in the cliff, spread rapidly as if the solid rock were dissolving. The cliff crumbled above it and collapsed, smashing down on the Terror Fish and burying it deep beneath thousand of tons of rock. *Stingray* cleared the canyon rim and sped back to Hawakiti.

"Phew!" gasped Phones, loosening his uniform

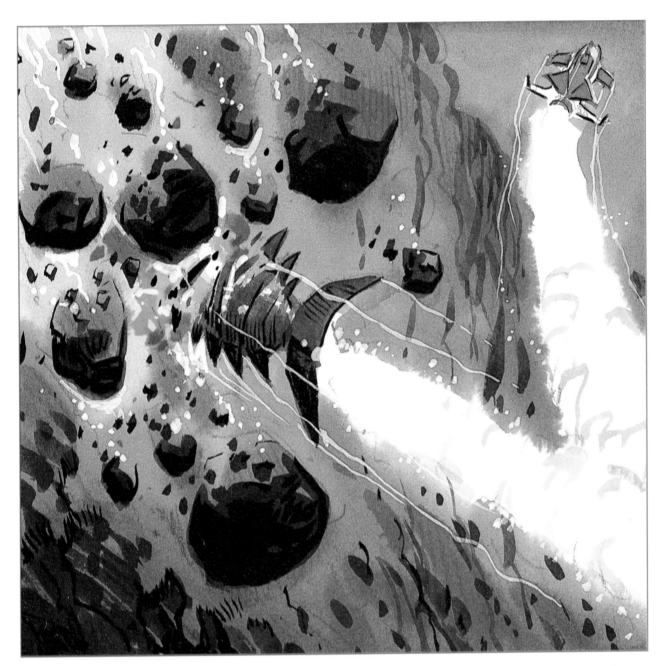

collar. "Sure got to hand it to you, Troy - making them destroy themselves. But what in the name of Neptune was that weapon?" Troy smiled. "Marina gave me the clue when she indicated she could hear it - but we couldn't hear a thing, Phones. It was a supersonic ray."

The dust fog was clearing by the time they reached the island. Miraculously, in spite of the enormous destruction of property, the casualties were light, for most of the holiday-makers had been on the beaches when the invisible terror struck. There were plenty of surface craft and planes on hand to help.

Troy returned to Marineville, where scientists confirmed his theory of a supersonic ray and set to work to perfect a defence against it in the event of Titan having another such weapon.

Commander Shore grinned grimly as he shook hands with Troy.

"So you're a budding boffin too, Tempest! But if those eggheads try to kid you to exchange that WASP uniform for a lab overall, they'll have a fight on their hands."

"You can say that again, father!" Atlanta said. And the smiling faces of Marina and Phones showed that the Commander wouldn't want for allies!

THE END

WASP AGENT'S TEST NO.2

This is the second of the tests to discover if you are a good **WASP Agent**. What you have to do is study the words below then re-arrange the letters to discover the names of some of the creatures Troy and his friends often see beneath the waves.

BOTTUR

STAKE

DOC

SMOLAN

ROLBEST

MALC

shodfig

barc

GRAYTINS

SLUSEM

LEHAW

HARKS

ghirren

Solution on page 45.

Using the code printed below, Marineville wants you to decipher the coded message sent by Troy Tempest to the Control Tower during a dangerous mission.

WASP AGENT'S TEST
NO.3

A	=	Å	J	=	Ô	R	= Â
B	=	1	K	=	*	S	= ß
C	=	Ç	L	=	Ò	T	= t
D	=	Î	M	=	¡	U	= ¶
E	=	‰	N	=	•	V	= √
F	=	Ï	O	=	Ø		
G	=	©	P	=	π	W	= Σ
H	=	Ó	Q	=	œ	X	= §
I	=	È				Y	= ¥

tÓ‰ t‰ÂÂøÂ ÏÈßÓ Èß

ÂÈ©Ót 1‰ÓÈ•Î ¶ß. ÏÈÂÈ•©©

ßtÈ•©© ¡ÈßßÈÒ‰ •øΣ.

Â‰π∆Ât ‰•Îß.

Solution on page 45

43

WASP AGENT'S TEST NO.4

The fourth Agent's challenge from Marineville. How quickly can you find the following words which are hidden in the grid below. Words can read diagonally, up, down, forwards and backwards.

Solution on page 45

SHORE   TEMPEST   TROY   ATLANTA   APHONY   PHONES   TITAN   LEMOY
MARINA   SAM   SURFACE   AGENT   MARINEVILLE   WASPS   FISHER   HYDROMIC
MISSILE   COMMANDER   SPY   STING   SEA   WAVE   SCARE

```
S A M S U R F A C E A
H T E M P E S T O G G
O L I W A V E R M M E
R A A N T T O M I N
E N A N G G I Y A S T
P T O B F Y T S N S O
M A R I N A A P D I F
S E A P H O N Y E L I
P H O N E S C A R E S
H Y D R O M I C R L H
M A R I N E V I L L E
L E M O Y W A S P S R
```

44

ANSWERS TO WASP AGENTS' TEST No.1.

1. 600 knots.
2. Marineville
3. X20
4. House of Lemoy
5. Titanica
6. Commander Shore, Atlanta, Lt. Fisher
7. Captain
8. Mechanical Fish
9. Aquatraz
10. Marina's father
11. Pacifica
12. Samuel Arthur

ANSWERS TO TEST NO. 4

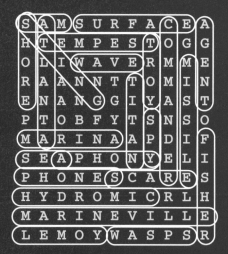

ANSWERS TO WASP AGENTS' TEST No.2.

Herring, Crab, Dogfish, Mussel, Shark, Salmon, Lobster, Coral, Whale, Stingray, Shrimp, Skate, Clam, Cod, Turbot.

ANSWER TO WASP AGENTS' TEST No.3.

THE TERROR FISH IS RIGHT BEHIND US. FIRING STING MISSILE NOW. REPORT ENDS.

STINGRAY PEN

One of the dozen subterranean compartments beneath the Marineville complex, the Stingray Pen has special air locks and flood gates. Accessible from the sea by means of a system of tunnels, the Pen is big enough to house several large craft. An elevator allows Stingray to be raised above the water level. The Pen can also be pumped clear of water to carry out maintenance on Stingray "in the dry".

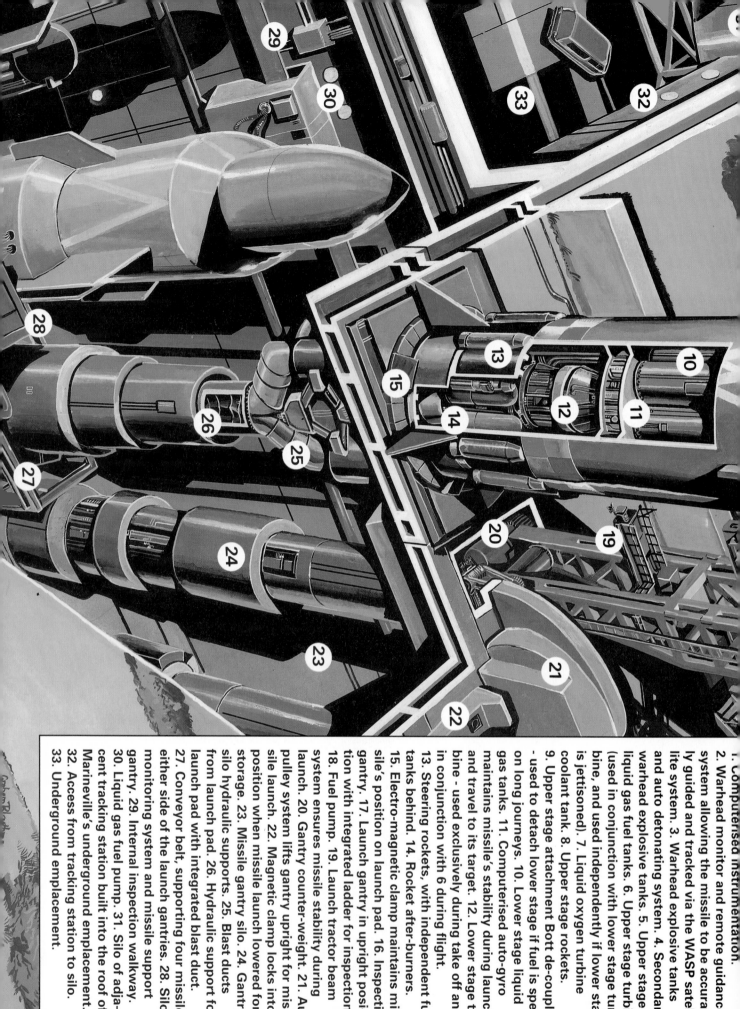

1. Computerised instrumentation.
2. Warhead monitor and remote guidance system allowing the missile to be accurately guided and tracked via the WASP satellite system. 3. Warhead explosive tanks and auto detonating system. 4. Secondary warhead explosive tanks. 5. Upper stage liquid gas fuel tanks. 6. Upper stage turbine (used in conjunction with lower stage turbine, and used independently if lower stage is jettisoned). 7. Liquid oxygen turbine coolant tank. 8. Upper stage rockets.
9. Upper stage attachment Bott de-coupler - used to detach lower stage if fuel is spent on long journeys. 10. Lower stage liquid gas tanks. 11. Computerised auto-gyro maintains missile's stability during launch and travel to its target. 12. Lower stage turbine - used exclusively during take off and in conjunction with 6 during flight.
13. Steering rockets, with independent fuel tanks behind. 14. Rocket after-burners.
15. Electro-magnetic clamp maintains missile's position on launch pad. 16. Inspection gantry. 17. Launch gantry in upright position with integrated ladder for inspections.
18. Fuel pump. 19. Launch tractor beam system ensures missile stability during launch. 20. Gantry counter-weight. 21. Auto pulley system lifts gantry upright for missile launch. 22. Magnetic clamp locks into position when missile launch lowered for storage. 23. Missile gantry silo. 24. Gantry silo hydraulic supports. 25. Blast ducts from launch pad. 26. Hydraulic support for launch pad with integrated blast duct.
27. Conveyor belt, supporting four missiles either side of the launch gantries. 28. Silo monitoring system and missile support gantry. 29. Internal inspection walkway.
30. Liquid gas fuel pump. 31. Silo of adjacent tracking station built into the roof of Marineville's underground emplacement.
32. Access from tracking station to silo.
33. Underground emplacement.

HYDROMIC MISSILES

Housed in a Cahelium-strengthened silo in front of the Control Tower, eight Hydromic Missiles form Marineville's primary ground to air firepower. Each missile has unique, though little used, optional two-stage travel capability. If long distance travel is required, the first stage or lower half of the rocket can be jettisoned when fuel is spent. The upper half continues the journey to the target. In general use, however, this has rarely been applied. The missiles, with their 25,000 mph Dyn-prop engines can be fitted with a number of warheads, including neutron and nuclear. They are constructed from Preferos and are powered by liquid gas.

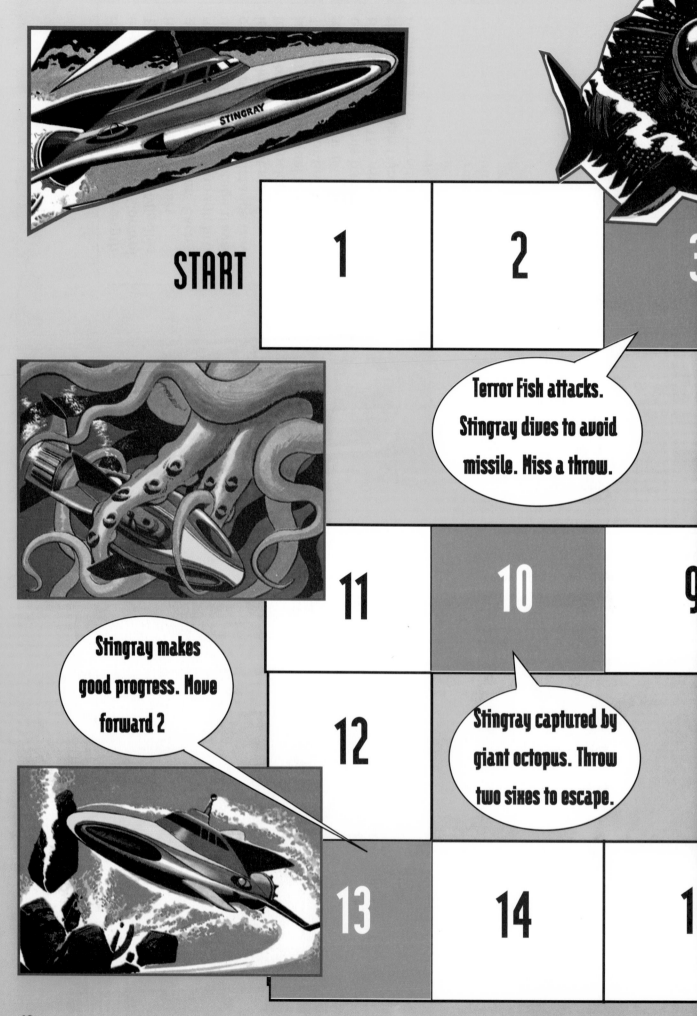

STINGRAY PATROL

HOW TO PLAY THIS EXCITING GAME

Stingray is off on another thrilling patrol. This game can be played by two or more players. To start, throw a six to open the Ocean Door and then travel with Troy and Phones through the dangers that lie ahead. The first player to arrive back at Marineville is the winner.

4	5
Terror Fish beaten off. Go forward 2 spaces.	6
8	7
16	**Throw 4 to finish.**

Rock-fall hits Stingray. Return to start, to Marineville for repairs.

FINISH

Continued from page 24

STINGRAY

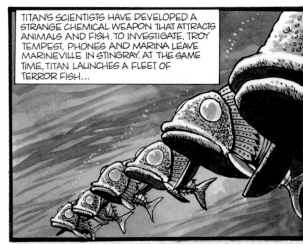

TITAN'S SCIENTISTS HAVE DEVELOPED A STRANGE CHEMICAL WEAPON THAT ATTRACTS ANIMALS AND FISH. TO INVESTIGATE, TROY TEMPEST, PHONES AND MARINA LEAVE MARINEVILLE IN STINGRAY. AT THE SAME TIME, TITAN LAUNCHES A FLEET OF TERROR FISH...

SAY, TROY—I'M PICKING UP SOME STRONG SIGNALS I FIGURE THERE ARE SIX VESSELS AHEAD...

CAN YOU TELL WHAT THEY ARE, PHONES?

I CAN'T BE CERTAIN, TROY, BUT MY GUESS IS THEY'RE TERROR FISH!

Script by Alan Fennell   Art: Keith Page

THE BATTLE RAGES... AND STINGRAY IS TOO FAST FOR THE TERROR FISH...

BEHIND US, SKIPPER! WE'RE IN DIRECT LINE OF FIRE!

HOLD ON! I DON'T THINK WE'RE GONNA SHAKE 'EM THIS TIME!

NEXT SECOND...

YOU'RE GUESS IS RIGHT, PHONES! BATTLE STATIONS! PRIME STING MISSILES!

MISSED! FIRE ONE, PHONES, NOW!

Subject: Aphony
Age: 100 marine years
Position: Father of Marina and emperor of underwater city Pacifica.
Ambition: To unite the undersea races with a peace treaty. All but Titan have signed

Story: Alan Fennell Art: Keith Page

MARINEVILLE
FACT FILE
NO. 10

Subject: Hydromic Missiles
Purpose: Ground to air defence weapon
Construction: Preferos heat-resisting metals
Speed: 25,000 mph
Armament: Various warheads, including neutron and nuclear
Power: Dyno-prop engines
Fuel: Liquid gas
Location: Various Marineville sights

AFTER A FIERCE BATTLE WITH A FLEET OF TERROR FISH, STINGRAY IS FINALLY STRUCK BY TITAN'S LATEST WEAPON...

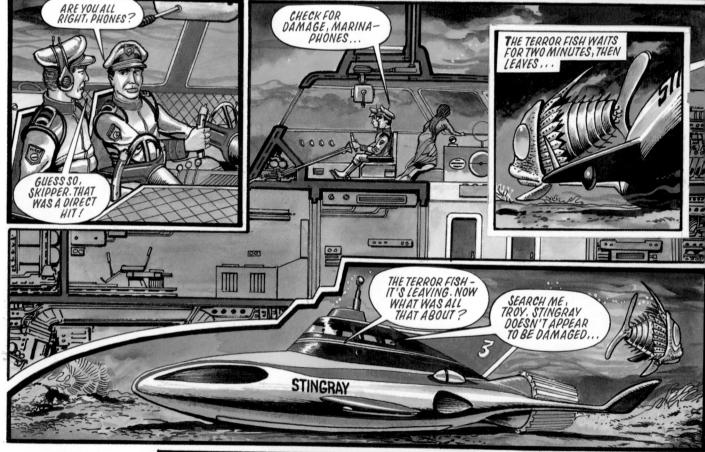

ARE YOU ALL RIGHT, PHONES?

GUESS SO, SKIPPER. THAT WAS A DIRECT HIT!

CHECK FOR DAMAGE, MARINA—PHONES...

THE TERROR FISH WAITS FOR TWO MINUTES, THEN LEAVES...

THE TERROR FISH — IT'S LEAVING. NOW WHAT WAS ALL THAT ABOUT?

SEARCH ME, TROY. STINGRAY DOESN'T APPEAR TO BE DAMAGED...

PHONES! THE ORANGE CLOUD! IT'S TITAN'S CHEMICAL WEAPON!

THE STRANGE SCENT DRIFTS THROUGH THE OCEAN...

...AND DRIFTS...AND DRIFTS...TO A DARK CAVE...

Story: Alan Fennell Art: Keith Page

Subject: Arrowhead
Interceptors
Purpose: Marineville
defence
Construction: Classified
Speed: 5,000 mph
Armament: Computer con-
trolled Thor 11 missiles,
F91 Seeker air to air rock-
ets, laser cannons
Power: Zeus afterburn
Turbofan rocket engine
Fuel: Classified fuel cells
and propellant
Location: Marineville's air-
base

MARINEVILLE FACT FILE NO. 11

STINGRAY HAS BEEN ATTACKED BY A TERROR FISH AND TITAN'S LATEST WEAPON, A STRANGE ORANGE CLOUD, SPREADS THROUGH THE SEA. THE CHEMICAL ATTRACTS SEA CREATURES BOTH LARGE AND SMALL...

MEANWHILE, STINGRAY LIES ON THE OCEAN BED, TEMPORARILY OUT OF ACTION...

STARTING ENGINES NOW, PHONES. LET'S HOPE THEY'RE NOT DAMAGED...

GUESS WE'RE OK, TROY.

YES, PHONES, BUT FOR HOW LONG? WHAT HAPPENS IF THOSE FISH DECIDE TO BLOCK THE JET INLETS?

CAPTAIN TEMPEST CONTACTS MARINEVILLE...

WE GET THE PICTURE, TROY. OUR SCIENTISTS ARE TRYING TO COME UP WITH A METHOD TO GET RID OF THOSE FISH...

THE COMMANDER IS RIGHT!

Script by Alan Fennell   Art: Keith Page

PLOTTING ROOM

IN THE MEANTIME, YOU TRY TO GET BACK TO MARINEVILLE – YOU NEVER KNOW WHAT'S HEADING YOUR WAY!

AND AT THAT MOMENT, IN TITANICA...

EXCELLENT! STINGRAY WILL SOON BE OUT OF COMMISSION...

STINGRAY

...AND MARINEVILLE WILL BE AT MY MERCY!

Subject: Control Room
Purpose: Monitoring status of all WASP vessels and aircraft, communications centre for WASP operations and activities
Equipment: Automatic Sea Map, used to track the course of vessels at sea; Locator Compass, can pinpoint the exact bearing and location of WASP vessels; Tunnel scanner, allows observation of link with ocean
Location: Marineville main building

TITAN'S NEWEST WEAPON, A STRANGE ORANGE CLOUD, ATTRACTS SHOALS OF SEA CREATURES TO STINGRAY. THEN, WITH THE SUPER SUB SWAMPED, TROY CANNOT STOP A FLEET OF TERROR FISH HEADING FOR MARINEVILLE...

LEFT BEHIND, STINGRAY ATTRACTS ANOTHER UNWELCOME VISITOR...

IT'S NO GOOD – THE FISH ARE BLOCKING THE POWER PLANT INLETS. THE THRUSTERS WON'T OPERATE!

WE'RE IN TROUBLE IF THAT MONSTER GRABS US!

THERE'S ONE CHANCE, PHONES. BLOW ALL TANKS – GET TO THE SURFACE FAST!

Script by Alan Fennell   Art: Keith Page

WITH A MIGHTY RUSH OF BUBBLES, THE BUOYANCY TANKS ARE EMPTIED...

AS THEY HURTLE TO THE SURFACE, TROY CONTACTS MARINEVILLE...

YES, TROY – WE'VE JUST DETECTED THE THE TERROR FISH FLEET! I'M SOUNDING BATTLE STATIONS NOW!

AS THE RAPID DRUM-BEATS SOUND OUT, MARINEVILLE SINKS...

THAT OCTOPUS HAS A REAL FIRM GRIP! WE'RE BEING DRAGGED UNDER, PHONES!

Subject: Standby Lounge
Purpose: Room where aquanauts wait for mission duties
Equipment: Extensive book, film and music library; full range of audio and video facilities, to assist personnel to relax before operations
Location: Marineville main building

A STRANGE ORANGE CLOUD, DEVISED BY TITAN'S SCIENTISTS, HAS ATTRACTED SEA CREATURES TO STOP STINGRAY OPERATING. WHILE A TERROR FISH FLEET HEADS FOR MARINEVILLE, A GIANT OCTOPUS GRIPS STINGRAY AS THE SUPER SUB SHOOTS TO THE SURFACE...

HANG ON, PHONES—MARINA!

WE'VE GOT TO SHAKE OFF THIS BEAUTY...

BUT HOW, TROY?

Script by Alan Fennell   Art: Keith Page

MARINA DRAWS TROY'S ATTENTION TO THE GENERATING PLANT...

WHAT IS IT, MARINA? WHAT ARE YOU TRYING TO TELL US?

ATOMIC GENERATOR DANGER 20,000 VOLTS

THEN TROY REALISES...

OF COURSE! WE COULD FIX THE BATTERIES TO MAKE STINGRAY ONE HUGE ELECTRICAL POWER SOURCE. WE CAN SHOCK THE OCTOPUS AWAY WITH CONTROLLED CHARGES...

BUT THAT WOULD KILL US, TROY!

ONLY IF WE WERE INSIDE STINGRAY. COME ON LET'S RIG UP THE POWER...

A LITTLE LATER...

WHEN THEY ARE CLEAR, TROY OPERATES A REMOTE-CONTROL SWITCH...

Subject: Injector seats
Purpose: To convey *Stingray* crew to the Pen
Mechanism: Hydraulic elevators attached to injection tubes
Location: In Standby Lounge, Marineville main building

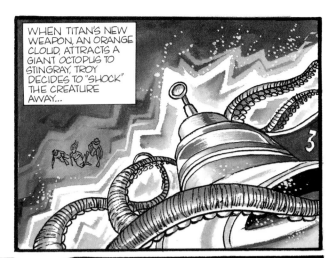

WHEN TITAN'S NEW WEAPON, AN ORANGE CLOUD, ATTRACTS A GIANT OCTOPUS TO STINGRAY, TROY DECIDES TO "SHOCK" THE CREATURE AWAY...

THE ELECTRIC CHARGE FORCES THE OCTOPUS TO RELEASE ITS GRIP...

TROY, PHONES AND MARINA WAIT FOR THE CHARGE TO CLEAR...

OK, PHONES. LET'S GET BACK ABOARD.

SURE THING, TROY...

Script by Alan Fennell   Art: Keith Page

TROY OPERATES THE CONTROLS...

WE HAVE TO GET BACK TO MARINEVILLE BEFORE THAT TERROR FISH FLEET ATTACKS!

YEAH, TROY... AND WE'D BETTER MAKE IT AT RATE SIX TO STOP THE FISH GATHERING AGAIN!

AS STINGRAY APPROACHES THE OCEAN DOOR...

Subject: House of Lemoy

Purpose: Suspected headquarters of Titanica surface agent X-20

Equipment: Complex computers, scanners and control systems - can be concealed at the touch of a button

Location: In Island of Lemoy, close to area of Marineville's Ocean Door

STINGRAY HAS BEEN OUT OF COMMISSION WHILE TROY, PHONES AND MARINA DEAL WITH A STRANGE ORANGE CLOUD THAT ATTRACTS UNDERSEA CREATURES. TITAN HAS USED THE TIME TO SEND A FLEET OF TERROR FISH TO ATTACK MARINEVILLE...

THERE ARE TOO MANY OF THEM FOR US, PHONES. BACK OFF. WE'LL HAVE TO CONTACT MARINEVILLE FOR ORDERS.

IN ITS UNDERGROUND EMPLACEMENT, MARINEVILLE IS SO FAR SAFE FROM TITAN'S MISSILES...

STINGRAY TO TOWER. WE'RE NOT FAR FROM FROM THE OCEAN DOOR...

Script by Alan Fennell   Art: Keith Page

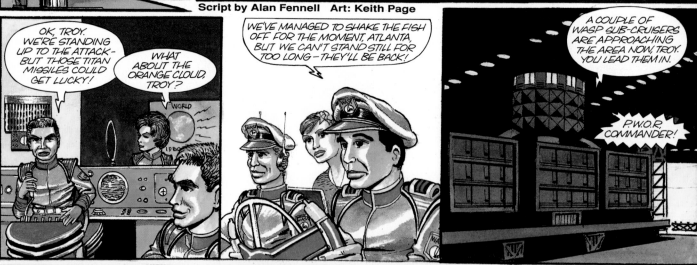

OK, TROY. WE'RE STANDING UP TO THE ATTACK - BUT THOSE TITAN MISSILES COULD GET LUCKY!

WHAT ABOUT THE ORANGE CLOUD, TROY?

WE'VE MANAGED TO SHAKE THE FISH OFF FOR THE MOMENT, ATLANTA, BUT WE CAN'T STAND STILL FOR TOO LONG - THEY'LL BE BACK!

A COUPLE OF WASP SUB-CRUISERS ARE APPROACHING THE AREA NOW, TROY. YOU LEAD THEM IN.

P.W.O.R, COMMANDER!

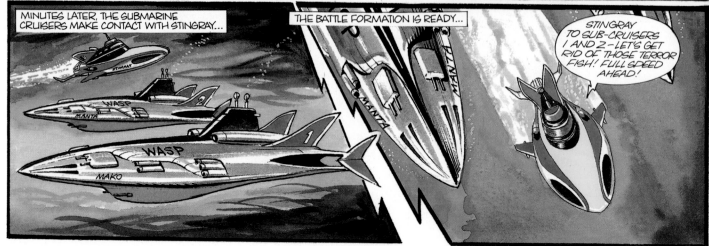

MINUTES LATER, THE SUBMARINE CRUISERS MAKE CONTACT WITH STINGRAY...

THE BATTLE FORMATION IS READY...

STINGRAY TO SUB-CRUISERS 1 AND 2 - LET'S GET RID OF THOSE TERROR FISH! FULL SPEED AHEAD!

MARINEVILLE
FACT FILE
NO. 17

Subject: X-20's Submarine
Purpose: To enable Titanica surface agent to carry out spying missions
Construction: Fused Coral Titanium
Speed: 500 plus knots
Armament: Three torpedo missiles
Power: Turbo aquajet
Fuel: Grenanol
Base: Underground pen below the House of Lemoy

TITAN'S TERROR FISH FLEET HAS MASSED TO TRY TO DESTROY MARINEVILLE. STINGRAY LINKS UP WITH TWO WASP SUBMARINE CRUISERS TO FIGHT OFF THE HOSTILE FORCE...

NO MATCH FOR MARINEVILLE'S DEFENCES, THE SURVIVING TERROR FISH RETREAT...

THEY'RE HEADING BACK TO TITANICA, PHONES. LET'S GO HOME!

STINGRAY CREW REPORT TO TOWER!

PEN 3 STINGRAY

ALL THREE OF YOU DID A FINE JOB...

GLAD TO BE OF ASSISTANCE, COMMANDER. NOW HOW ABOUT THAT ORANGE CLOUD?

MARINEVILLE SCIENTISTS HAVE FOUND AN ANTIDOTE, TROY. STINGRAY AND ALL WASP VESSELS WILL BE TREATED...

GREAT, ATLANTA. I WONDER HOW TITAN FEELS RIGHT NOW AFTER THE BEATING WE GAVE HIM?

YOU FOOL, GILFIN! YOU SAID THE ORANGE CLOUD WOULD STOP STINGRAY! TAKE HIM OUT OF MY SIGHT!

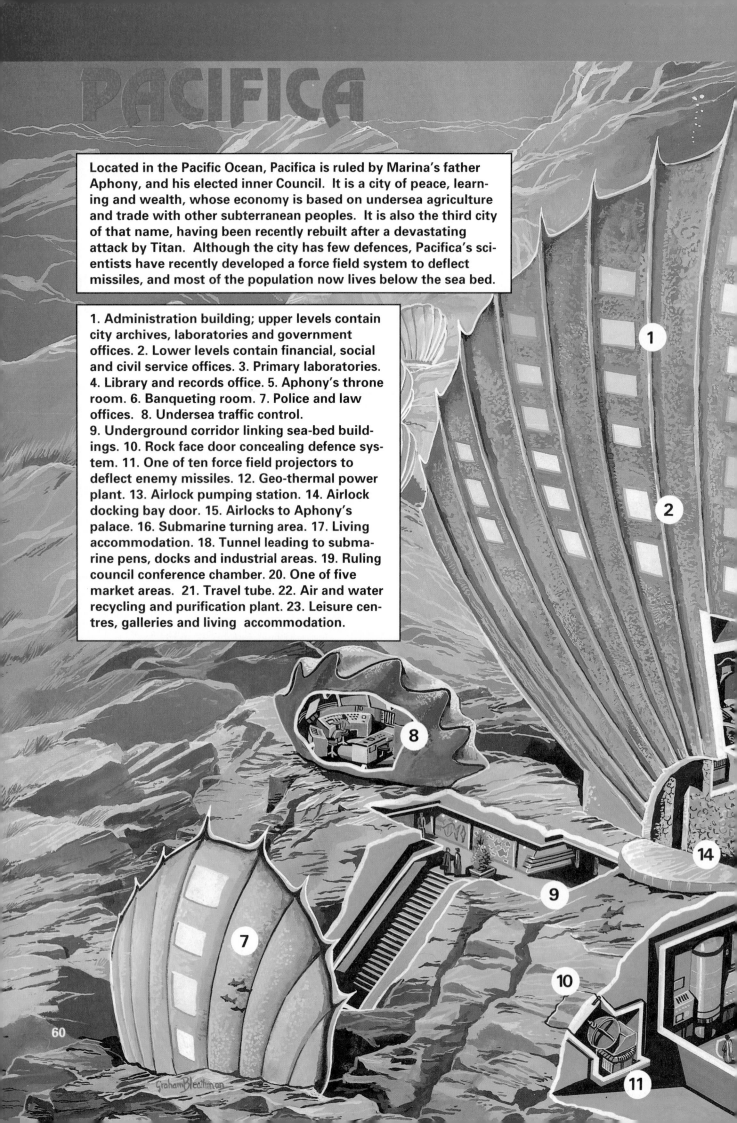

PACIFICA

Located in the Pacific Ocean, Pacifica is ruled by Marina's father Aphony, and his elected inner Council. It is a city of peace, learning and wealth, whose economy is based on undersea agriculture and trade with other subterranean peoples. It is also the third city of that name, having been recently rebuilt after a devastating attack by Titan. Although the city has few defences, Pacifica's scientists have recently developed a force field system to deflect missiles, and most of the population now lives below the sea bed.

1. Administration building; upper levels contain city archives, laboratories and government offices. 2. Lower levels contain financial, social and civil service offices. 3. Primary laboratories. 4. Library and records office. 5. Aphony's throne room. 6. Banqueting room. 7. Police and law offices. 8. Undersea traffic control.
9. Underground corridor linking sea-bed buildings. 10. Rock face door concealing defence system. 11. One of ten force field projectors to deflect enemy missiles. 12. Geo-thermal power plant. 13. Airlock pumping station. 14. Airlock docking bay door. 15. Airlocks to Aphony's palace. 16. Submarine turning area. 17. Living accommodation. 18. Tunnel leading to submarine pens, docks and industrial areas. 19. Ruling council conference chamber. 20. One of five market areas. 21. Travel tube. 22. Air and water recycling and purification plant. 23. Leisure centres, galleries and living accommodation.

Graham Bleathman

61